BLUE FROG

ISBN 0-919673-95-3

Printed by Derksen Printers. Steinbach. Manitoba Canada

This book is dedicated to
Donna, Ethel and Sharen
who help make dreams come true.

Acknowledgement

Reprinted with permission
"Blue Frog"
From Reading in Science Series
Copyright © 1980 Peguis Publishers

A special thank you to those who listened to these poems as they were being born, for their encouragement and for their breathing life into these poems by using them with children. And to Alice, who was never too busy to type a poem for a frantic poet.

Contents

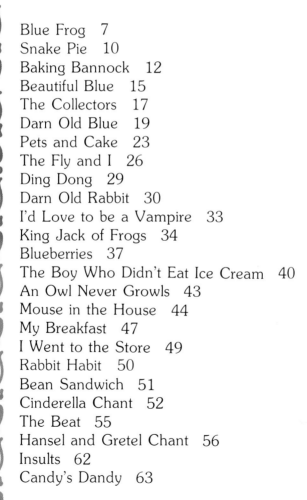

Blue Frog

This is a weird tale, and it makes me wail,
And I think it will make you shiver,
Of a very strange frog, sitting on a log
By the banks of an enchanted river.

A prince called Larry had promised to marry
A princess of riches and fame.
She was rather large, sort of built like a barge,
And Gwendolyn was her name.

Now, Larry was kind, but he did change his mind,
And decided he'd rather not marry.
Though the princess was rich, she looked like a witch,
So away ran our gallant prince, Larry.

Now, our princess true was feeling so blue
Because she had no prince to marry.
And she would often cry and she'd wish to die,
So in love was she with Prince Larry.

Then one fine day, with the prince still away,
Gwendolyn heard a very strange story
Of how a spell was cast, in days not long past,
Changing a prince to a frog. Oh, how gory!

So she went to look and carefully took
The path to the enchanted river.
There she found a blue frog, perched on a log.
This made our "fair" princess quiver.

Could this be Larry, the prince she would marry?
A beat of her heart she did miss.
To change the frog back to a prince, alack,
She must give the blue frog a kiss.

So she jumped on the log, and kissed the blue frog,
And breathlessly waited for Larry.
The minutes went by, and the hours did fly,
Still a blue frog in her hand she did carry.

Then she let out a sigh, and softly did cry,
For she knew the blue frog was not Larry.
A blue frog would not do, and she hopelessly knew
That a prince she never would marry.

So home from the bog, with the frog from the log,
To her kitchen with haste she did flee.
And the blue frog she ate, he tasted just great,
Washed down with a nice cup of tea.

It is sad to say, but I'll tell you today,
If my secret you promise to carry.
Two kisses indeed, not just one did she need,
To change that blue frog back to Larry.

This was a strange tale, and it did make me wail,
And I think it did make you shiver.
Oh, that poor strange blue frog who sat on that log
By the banks of that enchanted river.

Snake Pie

Oh my, oh my, I gotta have my old snake pie
You can have your worm soup
Or your toasted fly
But I gotta have my old snake pie
SNAKE PIE.
Snake, snake, snake snake pie
SNAKE PIE
Snake, snake, snake snake pie, oh my, oh my
You gotta try my old snake pie
Snake PIE.

Eddie Zlick eats his worms on toast
He — thinks — it's the most
But all he could do was sit and sigh
When I showed him some of my old snake pie
SNAKE PIE

The principal, he sat down to eat
So I slips him a special treat
Oh my, oh my, I thought he'd die
When he found he was eating my old snake pie
Snake PIE

Mary Meekis ate a toasted fly
She said — everyone should try
To catch and toast a big old fly
Oh my, oh my, I'll stick, to my old snake pie
Snake PIE.

My teacher's name is Mrs. Fry.
She said that she'd like to buy
A pound and a quarter of my old snake pie
Then we ate it, she and I.
SNAKE PIE

Principals, they're really mean
On snake pie they are not keen
But my teacher, she's a doll
When we get snake pie we eat it all.
Snake pie.

Snake, snake, snake snake pie,
SNAKE PIE
Snake, snake, snake snake pie, oh my, oh my
SNAKE PIE!

Baking Bannock

I remember my mother at the kitchen table
Mixing bannock as only she was able.
Three cups of flour and some baking powder.
My stomach starts growling, louder and LOUDER.

REFRAIN:
Mmmm, Mmmm, it tastes so good
Bannock baked like my mother could
Into my mouth and down to my tummy
Mmmm, Mmmm, it tastes so yummy.

(Refrain to be repeated after each verse.)

Two tablespoons of lard, a dash of salt
My mother's making bannock with never a fault
Pour in some milk, it sure looks swell
Knead it, knead it, knead it well.

Pop it in the oven and wait for a while
Then out comes the bannock and we eat in style.
Oh, my, it sure is fine.
You have yours and I'll have mine.

My brother, Billy, is a bannock boy,
Eating bannock is his greatest joy.
My mother says "Billy, eat your bannock with jam
And you'll grow up to be a man."

My sister, Molly, makes bannock disappear
She's eaten only bannock for half a year.
"Give up my bannock, I'd rather be dead.
You eat the carrots, I'll eat bannock instead."

My Uncle David is strong as a horse.
He got that way by eating bannock o'course.
Bannock for breakfast and bannock for lunch
And for supper more bannock to munch.

My Aunt Mary is a bannock champ
She baked bannock in a lumber camp
But the men all quit, they just wouldn't stay
When the boss tried to take their bannock away.

And once in a while add sugar and raisin
Mom would bake bannock for a special occasion
And my mother she was always fair,
Everyone would have a share.

Sixteen kids could be in the house
They'd all have a share, and a crumb for the mouse.
My mother would smile and then she'd say,
"Eat your bannock and go out and play."

Now I make bannock as only I'm able,
Kneading the dough at the kitchen table,
And my children watch and hear me say,
"Eat your bannock and go out and play."

Beautiful Blue

t's true, it's true
That I love blue
In the winter or the summer
In the spring or the fall
Blue is the color
That's the very best of all.

Eyes of Blue
Sky of blue
Jeans of Blue
And water Blue
All these things of blue will do
'Cause blue is best of all.

Navy blue
Royal blue
Powder blue
And icy blue
Any shade of blue will do
'Cause blue is best of all.

Yellow, orange,
Brown and green
And red are colors too,
But they're never half as pretty
As any shade of blue.

It's true, it's true
That I love blue
In the winter or the summer
In the spring or the fall
Blue is the color
That's the very best of all.

Collectors

i.
I'm Paul
I'm a collector.
I collect stones and bones.
I collect marbles and string.
I collect stamps, bottle caps, and matchbook covers.
I collect any old thing.

Hi.
I'm marvelous Mary.
I'm a cute collector.
I collect dainty dolls and bouncy balls.
I collect green glass, jade jewellery and fancy fans.
I collect authentic autographs, pressed plants
And cuddly kittens.
I collect only interesting items.

Hi.
I'm a Martian.
I collect collectors.
And I've just collected you.

Darn Old Blue

This is the story of a man and his dog
who went one day for a hunt in the bog.
He took his gun and his rubbers too
And the name of his dog was Darn Old Blue.
Darn Old Blue, Darn Old Blue,
And the name of his dog was Darn Old Blue.

Grey squirrel sitting at the top of a tree
Bang goes the gun; watch him flee.
"Hey there man, it's just no fun
When you shoot at me with that old shotgun."
Old shotgun, old shotgun,
"When you shoot at me with that old shotgun."

Big bullfrog on a lily pad
The man and the dog what a chase they had.
The man and his dog they wound up wet.
The frog he croaked, "You ain't caught me yet."
Caught me yet, caught me yet
The frog he croaked, "You ain't caught me yet."

Red fox sitting by the edge of the bay
Along comes Blue and the fox doesn't stay.
"Hey there, dog, it's just no fun
When you chase after me and make me run."
Make me run, make me run.
"When you chase after me and make me run."

He saw an old cat by the big oak tree
With its tail in the air, the hunter could see
A big white stripe on a coat of black.
Then he shot at the cat and the cat shot back.
The cat shot back, the cat shot back
Then he shot at the cat and the cat shot back.

The old man missed but the cat shot true.
He sprayed that man and Darn Old Blue.
Oh, what a smell! Oh, how they stunk!
It's no fun to be shot by a darn old skunk.
Darn old skunk, darn old skunk,
It's no fun to be shot by a darn old skunk.

Home they ran, the man and his dog,
Passing the squirrel, the fox, and the frog.
And as they passed, I'll tell you true,
The man he stunk and so did Blue.
So did Blue, so did Blue.
The man he stunk and so did Blue.

When he got home he went in the door.
His wife took a smell and then she swore.
She chased him from the kitchen to the dining room.
Chased him from the house with her darn old broom.
Darn old broom, darn old broom,
Chased him from the house with her darn old broom.

This was the story of a man and his dog.
They slept all night in an old hollow log.
For when they got home his wife said, "Scat!"
Because he shot at that old pole cat.
Old pole cat, old pole cat,
Because he shot at that old pole cat.

Pets and Cake

y sister Sue, does she love cake
She eats as much, as Mom can bake.
She loves it chocolate, she likes it white.
She eats it every day and night.

But my sister Sue she hates my pets,
Every, single, one, I gets.
She hates my spider and my frog.
She even hates my cat and dog.

I put my fish into her bed
But only after it was dead.
My dog whose feet were caked with dirt.
He wiped them clean upon her skirt.

My cat had kittens in her hat.
My mother said 'enough of that'.
She said my pets must stay away
From my sister every day.

Today my frog got in her lunch.
When she bit her cake, it went crunch crunch,
What's worse than a frog inside your cake?
A half a frog in half your cake.

My sister screamed, my sister spit
And then she took a hairy fit.
Her eyes went red. I thought she'd choke.
I quickly said, "It was just a joke."

My sister said she'd tell my Dad.
I knew right then, I would be sad.
Then she spied my bag of lunch
And began to think of cake at once.

She said that we could make a deal
If I gave her my bag, she wouldn't squeal.
She wanted the cake that was inside.
"Oh please don't take it" I quickly cried.

"Yes, Yes" said she. "You give it here."
"You will not like it sister dear."
But my sister thinks that she's so wise
But I think she's in for a great surprise.

My sister smiled and grinned with glee.
She thought she'd got the best of me.
I sadly handed her that bag
And wiped my tears upon a rag.

My sister's in for one big fright
I'll prove her brother's always right.
'Cause in that bag there is no cake.
There's nothing there but my pet snake.

The Fly and I

I lay in my bed and I heard a buzz
I listened to hear just what it was.
It flew round the room, way up high
The buzz I heard was a darn old fly.

CHORUS
Buzz Buzz Buzz
Fly here and there
Buzz Buzz Buzz
Then land in my hair
Buzz Buzz Buzz
And away he goes
Buzz Buzz Buzz
Then he lands on my nose.

I jumped from my bed, turned on the light.
There was no fly anywhere in sight.
Turned out the light, jumped back in bed
And the fly went buzz, and flew round my head.

I lay on my side, and the fly buzzed by.
Can't get to sleep, no matter how I try.
I lay on my back, there's a buzz once more
I'll never get to sleep, no chance to snore.

I was awake all night, now I sure will try
To kill that fly, he will surely die.
Poison or a hammer or a swatter I'll use
No more sleep will this boy lose.

I got three spiders and let them free
I hoped they'd catch that fly for me.
I got sticky paper and a can of spray
I sprayed that room, all through the day.

I went to bed, tired as a dog.
I knew I'd sleep as sound as a log.
But that night there was no sleep because,
All of a sudden, I heard a buzz.

Ding Dong

Part 1   Ding dong, you're wrong
Snow white, I'm right.
Part 2   Green paint, no you ain't
Chocolate fudge, I'm the judge

Part 1   Red and white, makes me right
Black and blue, shame on you.
Part 2   Brown hood, you're no good.
Green flies, you tell lies.

Part 1   One two, to heck with you
Four three, hurray for me.
Part 2   Sides and ends, let's be friends.
Fish and tea, you and me.

Part 1   Nine eight, we're great
But ding dong, you're still wrong.

Darn Old Rabbit

arn old rabbit in the carrot patch
He's just too fast for the farmer to catch.
That rabbit can jump, can he ever run.
You'll never shoot him with your old shotgun.

That rabbit loves carrots and celery too,
He likes to eat lettuce and drink home brew.
He ate all the spinach and a field of grain.
"Look out farmer, here he comes again."

He chewed up the cabbage and he ate all the peas.
He stole all the honey from the farmer's bees.
He swallowed the turnips and he ate all the corn.
Farmer wished that he'd never been born.

Rabbit was saying "What's up Doc?"
I didn't know that rabbits could talk.
Rabbit said "Farmer I tell you now
I'm gonna eat your horse and cow."

And after he finished the horse and cow
He ate the buggy and he ate the plough.
That darn old rabbit, he was so cruel
He even ate the farmer's old mule.

He swallowed him whole, right down to his tummy
And as he went down he tasted real yummy
But then that mule began to kick
And the poor old rabbit felt mighty sick.

The mule kicked the rabbit right up to the moon
They ate green cheese with a long handled spoon.
He won't come back, I tell you true
But if he does, he might eat you.

CHORUS:
Sing runna runna
Ding Ding
Bang Boom
Sing runna runna
Dinga Ding
Bang Boom
Sing runna runna
Dinga Ding
Bang Boom
Dinga Ding
Dinga Bang
Dinga Ding Bang Boom

I'd Love to be a Vampire

f I were a vampire I'd love to fly
Over the graveyard way up high.
To scare some people sure would be fun.
I'd sneak up, say Boo, and watch them run.
My pointy teeth and my long black cape
Would make the people stare and gape,
And when I wanted I would change to a bat,
I'd fly in circles or chase a black cat.
And the name Count Dracula has a very nice ring,
Oh dear, I've just thought of an unfortunate thing,
For as a vampire I'd be a real dud
'Cause I really can't stand the sight of blood.

King Jack of the Frogs

'm going to catch me the king of the frogs
And put him inside of my pail.
He'll be sitting on top of a sunken log
And he'll be half as big as a whale.

His back will be green, of an emerald hue
All covered with spots of deep black,
With belly of white, and tongue of dark blue
And I'm going to call him King Jack.

King Jack of the Frogs, he sits on those logs
And catches big horseflies for lunch.
Mosquitoes and gnats, as big as black bats
And he swallows them down in a bunch.

He leaps in the air, and he swallows them there,
He's a terror to bugs of all kinds.
Beatles and worms, he swallows in turns
And I'm quite sure that nobody minds.

When I capture King Jack, I'll take him right back
To my home, as a pet for my yard.
There'll be no mosquitoes in sight, when I sit out at night
And my can of fly spray I'll discard.

But it wouldn't be fair, so I'll leave him right there
In his home on those old sunken logs.
He'll be happy and proud, and croak very loud,
Majestic, King Jack of the Frogs.

Blueberries

Did you ever eat blueberries with sugar and cream?
They melt in your tummy and taste like a dream.
Bake them in muffins, in bannock or cake.
Blueberries taste good in whatever you bake.

REFRAIN:
Blueberries, blueberries, big and fat.
Me and my sister and her old grey cat
Pick them and eat them or put them in a pail.
Yes sir, yes sir, they're for sale.

We went to pick blueberries, one day in July
The breeze was gentle and the sun was high.
I took along my pail and my old brown hat,
I took my little sister, and her old grey cat.

I found a plant with a berry or two,
Big and fat and deep deep blue.
My sister picked lots and I found more.
I put two in my pail and then ate four.

I picked those berries, seven hundred and three.
Not many for the pail, but lots for me.
My tummy got full, couldn't eat another one,
So I filled up my pail — just for fun.

My sister said Joey, look what I see,
Cute little bear cubs, one, two, three.
They were cute and cuddly and furry and round.
Then all of a sudden came a frightening sound.

A big mother bear, charged into view.
I ran very fast, and so would you.
We climbed up a tree, in three seconds flat,
Me and my sister, and her old grey cat.

Then the bear ambled off, gave her cubs a slap
Then she took them home, for their afternoon nap.
We climbed down the tree and grabbed our pail.
We sure better run, better hit the trail.

My sister sold blueberries by the side of the road
But I went to play, and I caught a toad.
I played all day, and did I have fun
But my sister had money, and I had none.

My sister said "Joey, I'll buy you a treat."
And that blueberry ice cream sure was neat.
Then we went home and fell asleep like that,
Me and my sister and her old grey cat.

The Boy who didn't Eat Ice Cream

om says that ice cream is good for you.
She says that it is nutritious.
But she said that about carrots too
And they certainly ain't delicious.

I like to do what I am told
And listen to my mummy.
Is there any kind of ice cream sold
That really does taste yummy?

Chocolate, lemon, peppermint candy,
Raspberry, Strawberry, Spumoni too.
Vanilla, pistachio, and moca tastes dandy.
Coffee, butterscotch and licorice blue.

I really cannot pick just one
So I think I'll try them all.
Thirty flavors really would be fun
And stack up, oh, so tall.

One lick, two licks, three licks, four.
This ice cream sure tastes great.
Five licks, six licks, seven licks more
Hey! ice cream I don't hate.

Twenty flavors and I'm getting full,
But eating I will not stop.
My shirt gets tight, it starts to pull.
My buttons start to pop.

At twenty-five I'm set to burst
But there are only five to go.
To eat thirty flavors I am the first
And this I truly know.

I'm turning green, and feeling blue.
I'm sicker than a dog.
I really wish, I'm telling you
I wasn't such a hog.

I was the first to eat ice cream
Thirty flavors at a time.
I really wish it was a dream
And the record wasn't mine.

If there's one thing I wish I'd never done
It was to be the very first
For of all the things I hate the most.
Carrots ain't the worst.

An Owl Never Growls

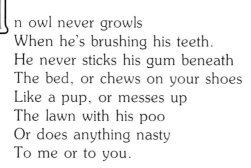An owl never growls
When he's brushing his teeth.
He never sticks his gum beneath
The bed, or chews on your shoes
Like a pup, or messes up
The lawn with his poo
Or does anything nasty
To me or to you.

An owl always tries
To be clever, sagacious and wise.
He loves his mother.
He is kind to his brother.
He respects his nephew, uncle and aunt.
But an owl never growls
When he's brushing his teeth
'Cause he can't.

Mouse in the House

here's a grey mouse, in our house,
He has whiskers so neat, and four dainty feet.
Running over the floor, to the big pantry door
With a smile that says please, as he nibbles our cheese.
But he'd better beware, of the danger that's there
And watch out for the snap, of Daddy's big trap.

Oh, Daddy, please please, what's a small bit of cheese?
Can we keep him my Dad, it would make me so sad
To kill that poor mouse, whose a guest in our house?
Put the trap far away, please let this mouse stay.
What's one small grey mouse, in our great big white house.
He's so gentle and sweet, and his manners are neat.

Now there are two little mice, they're so pretty and nice
As they scamper and play, please Dad can they stay?
Now the mice number four, and they play on the floor.
They love to play tag, or hide in Mom's bag.
Oh isn't it great, the mice number eight!
They're in my Dad's boot, with their babies so cute.

Sixteen little mice, got into our spice.
They ate all the pears, and chewed my stuffed bears.
They're not as cute as they was, and that is because
I've just counted thirty-two, and I'm feeling so blue
For they ate all my toast, and the jam I love most.
They nibbled the fish, in Mom's casserole dish.

There's sixty-four, by the door,
They've chewed up the drapes, and eaten the grapes.
One hundred twenty-eight, on Dad's breakfast plate.
They devoured the rice, those darn little mice.
Now a thousand or more, they cover the floor.
A million I see, they're up to my knee.

My Dad thought and thought, then a big cat he bought.
That great big tom cat, did he ever get fat
As he ate all those mice, he did it so nice
With never a burp, or a noisy wet slurp.
Now there's never a mouse, in our great big white house.
But now there are TWO cats . . . !

My Breakfast

 onday morning, I ate my breakfast
Ham, jam and a big pancake.

Tuesday morning, I had a glass of juice
Ham, jam and a big pancake.

Wednesday morning I had some prunes
A glass of juice,
Ham, jam and a big pancake.

Thursday morning, I ate three fried eggs
Prunes and juice,
Ham, jam and a big pancake.

Friday morning, I had some bacon,
Three fried eggs,
Prunes and juice,
Ham, jam and a big pancake.

Saturday morning, I ate some French toast,
Bacon and eggs,
Prunes and juice,
Ham, jam and a big pancake.

Sunday morning, I ate oatmeal
Some French toast, bacon and eggs,
Prunes and juice,
Ham, jam and a big pancake.

On Monday morning I will eat
Ham, jam and a big pancake.
What kind of a breakfast will you make?

I Went to the Store

went to the store to buy some meat
And the butcher's name o'course was Pete.

I went to the store to buy some bread
And the baker's name o'course was Fred.

I went to the store to buy me a pill
And the pharmacist's name o'course was Jill.

I went to the store to buy me a toy
And the sales clerk's name o'course was Roy.

I went to the store to buy some barley
And the grocer's name o'course was Charlie.

I went to the store to buy some glue
And the sales lady's name o'course was Sue.

I went to the store to buy some candy
And the salesman's name o'course was Andy.

I went to the store to buy some pants
and the tailor's name o'course was Vance.

I went to the store to buy some beer
And the storekeeper said, "Get out of here!"

Rabbit Habit

f a rabbit you should get
Be sure he'll make a perfect pet
But he may have a few bad habits
Like producing other rabbits.

Steve was what I named my bunny
Six more rabbits! Something's funny.
But if that's too much for you
Please don't worry — Rabbit Stew.

Bean Sandwiches

on't knock it till you try it
Take your baloney and you fry it
Put the beans in a baking pot
And you stir them till they're hot.

Add some ketchup and some spice
And some mustard would be nice.
Then you stir it round and round
Chop the baloney, add a pound.

Add some soya, and some cheese
And some syrup if you please.
Stir it once, stir it twice
And it smells, so very nice.

Brown bread is my pick
Spread the butter very thick.
Then I put the beans on top
And I never, never stop
Till I've eaten every bite
'Cause it tastes so very right.

Bean sandwiches are yummy
And they fill up, all my tummy.
Try them once, try them twice
Bean sandwiches are nice.

Cinderella Chant

his is the story of poor Cinderella,
Who cooked and sewed and scrubbed out the cellar.
She polished the silver and she took out the trash
But her sisters wouldn't take her to the big royal bash.

And so at home, Cinderella sat
Just her and eight mice and a big fat rat.
Then all of a sudden, in the room was a flash.
Fairy Godmother landed on the floor with a crash.

A coach from a pumpkin, its horses from the mice,
The rat became the coachman, he looked very nice,
And a beautiful gown, and slippers of glass.
"But leave on time, don't let midnight pass!"

The stepsisters came, they entered the ball.
The prince he saw them, turned his face to the wall.
"Oh, isn't that cute, he's flirting with me.
He loves me so, it's plain to see."

Cinderella appeared, she dazzled them all.
She danced with the prince, every dance at the ball.
The prince was ecstatic and as happy as a loon.
Then the clock struck twelve and she ran from the room.

The prince followed quickly but he was too late.
He saw a big pumpkin and some mice at the gate.
He saw a glass slipper, and a big fat rat
But no Cinderella, and that was that.

"Coachman, coachman, come here now.
Find that lady and I don't care how.
Use the glass slipper, but you better be sure
When you find that lady I will marry her."

They tried on that slipper, every girl in the land.
To fit that slipper would surely be grand.
Till they came at last to the last little shack
But the mean stepmother held Cinderella back.

The ugly stepsisters tried on that shoe
"Give it to me, it won't fit you."
Anastasia tried it on but a toe stuck out
"Hack it right off," Anastasia did shout.

"That shoe doesn't fit, is there one more girl?"
"There's no one else here, I tell you sir."
Then a very loud sneeze was heard by all
And out from the closet came the GIRL FROM THE BALL

She tried on the slipper, and it did fit
The ugly stepsisters were sure in a snit
Cinderella and the prince were married in June
And they danced all night by the light of the moon.

So all you pretty girls, I tell you the true
Keep polishing silver, do cooking too
And your ugly stepsisters will cry boo-hoo
When your fairy godmother makes your dreams come true

The Beat

Jumping to the right beat
Jumping with my two feet
It's really neat — — to get the beat, — —
Got the beat in my feet
Now it's moving to my seat
I got the beat!
— — — — .

Shake around your left hand
Try to do a handstand
It's really grand — — to shake your hand — —
In your hand is the beat
And you really do it neat.
You got the beat!
— — — —

Moving to the right sound
The beat is what we found.
It's all around — — this beat we've found — —
Now this beat is a treat
For everyone we meet.
We got the beat!
— — — —

Hansel and Gretel Chant

Narrators 1:   Gretel and Hansel were a girl and a boy
Their family was poor, they never had a toy.
They were both very hungry, no food in the house
Not even enough, for a wee small mouse.

Brooms in the city, their parents did sell,
But not very many, they didn't do well
Mom and Dad: "Make more brooms, while we are away
Work very hard, and don't you play!"

Narrators 1:   But Hansel sang while Gretel played
And all day long no brooms were made
Mom came home, was she ever mad
Mom: "Get rid of those kids", she said to Dad.

Hansel: "To get us lost in the woods, father will try
Come on Gretel, please don't cry
We'll leave a trail of pebbles, along the way
Then we'll follow them home," Hansel did say.

Narrators 2:   Father took them to the woods, that very day
And Hansel left pebbles, along the way
Then Father vanished, right out of sight,
But they followed the pebbles, and got home that night.

So father took them out, again next day
They left a trail of crumbs, along the way
But the birds ate the crumbs and they were gone
So lost in the woods they travelled on.

Then they saw a house in the middle of the wood,
And to the children, it sure looked good.
Gingerbread men, in great big rings
And the house was made of the following things.

All: Gumdrops, ju jubes, lollipops too
Shortbread, gingerbread, icing of blue,
Toffee, licorice, peppermint candy
The house looked great, and it tasted dandy.

Narrators 1:	To a mean old witch, the house did belong,
	Her teeth were yellow, her breath was strong
Witch:	"Who's nibbling on my house," the witch did say
Narrators:	Then she grabbed them both, they couldn't get away.

The witch was mean, she was short and fat
She rode on a broom, and owned a black cat
She had a wart on her chin, black hair in her nose
How many children she had eaten, no one knows.

Witch:	"Clean out the oven and fill up the kettle
	Work you lazy girl," she said to Gretel,
	"And we'll feed your brother ten times a day
	Cook up more food, there's no time to play."

Narrators 1:	She put Hansel in a cage and fed him well
	Then her plans for him, she did tell
Witch:	"Eat more food, get nice and fat
	Then I'll pop you in the oven, and that will be that."

Narrators 1:	The witch was nearsighted, she didn't see well
	She would pinch Hansel's arm, so she could tell
	If he was fat enough, for her to bake,
	But he seemed to stay thin, just like a rake.
	He used an old chicken bone, for her to feel
	It wasn't his arm, it wasn't real
	He fooled that witch for a week and day
	Till she said she'd cook him anyway.
Witch:	"Gretel, Gretel, come here right away.
	Light up the oven, do what I say.
	The flames will roar, what a beautiful sight
	Now test the oven, see if it's right."
Gretel:	"How will I test it?" asked Gretel with a sigh.
	"I don't know how —", she did lie.
Witch:	"Just open the door, I'll show you how
	It seems to be ready, I'll cook him now."

Narrators 2:   As the witch bent over, to look inside,
Gretel gave her a push, she gave her a ride,
Into the oven with the flames and the heat.
Then the witch blew up, boy that was neat.

Then the gingerbread men, all twenty five,
They all began to dance, they all came alive.
They'd all been children, that the witch did bake
But when the old witch died, the spell did break.

All: Now this story has a happy ending,
No more witch, nor brooms for mending
Hansel and Gretel, they became bakers.
Selling gingerbread houses, are there any takers?

Gumdrops, ju jubes, lollipops too,
Shortbread, gingerbread, icing of blue,
Toffee, licorice, peppermint candy,
Their houses look great and they taste real dandy!

Insults

I took the teeth from a crocodile
As he slithered and blithered along the Nile.
Then I took the head of a Koala bear
And an oranguatang donated his hair
And I stuck on the nose of an elephant
And the ears I made from a dumbcame plant.
Then I added the neck of a large giraffe.
When I put them together they made me laugh.
Then a fat pig's back and a camel's hump
And kangaroo's legs to make him jump.
Then a long rat tail and the feet of a duck
Then I added a beard of manure and muck.
I stood back to look at just what I had made.
It was so gruesome I was really afraid.
But then I laughed for I knew what it was.
I was no longer afraid and that was because
I had tried to create a creature new
But the darn thing turned out to look like you.

Candy's Dandy

uick, pick
A peppermint stick.
Lick it and taste it
And put it in your tummy.
Peppermint, peppermint tastes so yummy.

Buy, try
A licorice whip
Chomp it and chew it
And put it in your tummy
Licorice, licorice tastes so yummy.

You, chew
A chocolate candy
Scrunch it and eat it
And put it in your tummy
Chocolate, chocolate tastes so yummy.